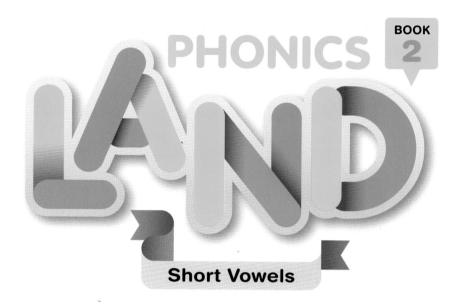

PHONICS **BOOK 2**

LAND

Short Vowels

YBM

Book 2

Contents

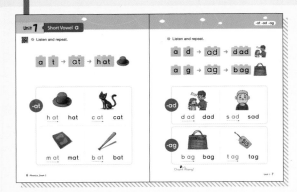

Letters and Sounds
New target combinations of sounds and related words are introduced with pictures.

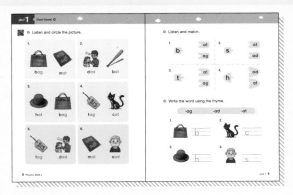

Practice 1
Children practice listening to the target words with the target sounds. They also practice identifying and writing the target sounds.

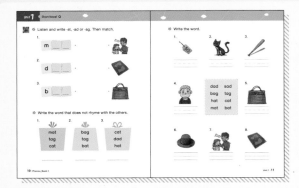

Practice 2
Children practice listening and writing the target sounds.

Activity
Children practice writing the target words in the activity.

Let's Read!
Children further practice the target words by reading a simple story.

Practice 3
Children confirm their understanding of the target words by writing the words in simple sentences.

Review & Challenge

The Review provides practice of the materials from the previous four units by using a variety of exercises focusing on the target sounds of letters and words.

The Challenge offers sessions to review the entire book. It reinforces students' phonics skills with various exercises and a test.

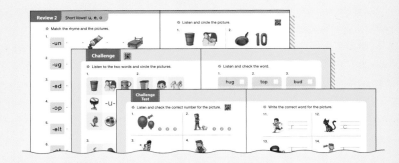

Special Features

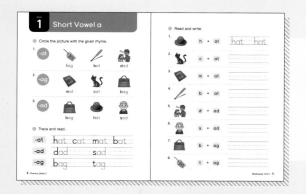

✦ Workbook ✦

Students review what they learned in class.
This can be used as homework or further practice.

✦ How to use QR codes ✦

Scan QR codes on the content pages, then you can use all of the listening sounds and flash animations, such as chants, stories, and listening questions.

e-learning

Scan e-learning QR codes, then you can use e-learning for self-study.

game

Scan game QR codes, then you can enjoy the phonics games.

◦ Note for Teachers ◦

The ultimate goal of the book is to help students be able to read and write words even if they encounter a new word. Therefore, students should be encouraged to listen and to identify the sounds of the letters, not to memorize the spellings of the words.

✿ Listen and repeat.

a t → at → h at 🎩

-at

h at   hat

c at   cat

m at   mat

b at   bat

✿ Listen and repeat.

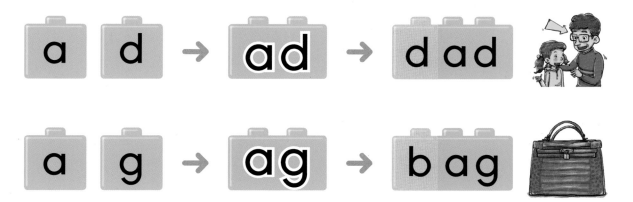

a   d → ad → d ad

a   g → ag → b ag

-ad

d ad   **dad**   s ad   **sad**

-ag

b ag   **bag**   t ag   **tag**

Chant Along!

✿ Listen and circle the picture.

1.

bag   mat

2.

dad   bat

3.

hat   bag

4.

tag   cat

5.

tag   dad

6.

mat   sad

✿ Listen and match.

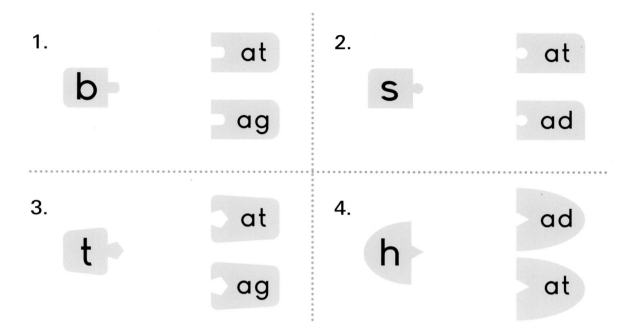

1.
b
at
ag

2.
s
at
ad

3.
t
at
ag

4.
h
ad
at

✿ Write the word using the rhyme.

-ag   -ad   -at

1.
b

2.
c

3.
h

4.
s

❀ Listen and write -at, -ad or -ag. Then match.

1.
m _____ _____

2.
d _____ _____

3.
b _____ _____

❀ Write the word that does not rhyme with the others.

1.

mat
tag
cat

2.

bag
tag
bat

3.

cat
dad
hat

✿ Write the word.

1.

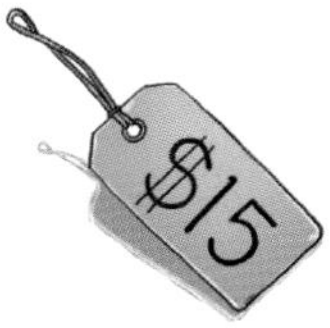

2.

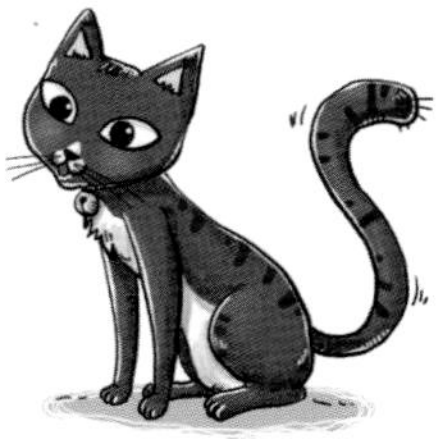

3.

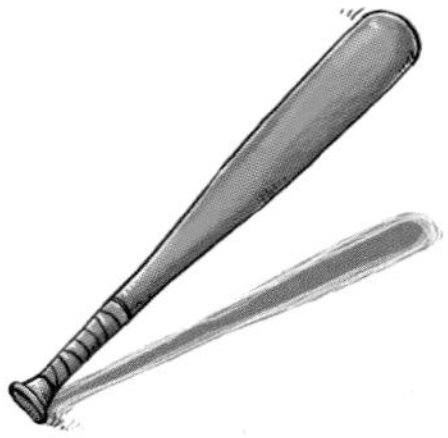

4.

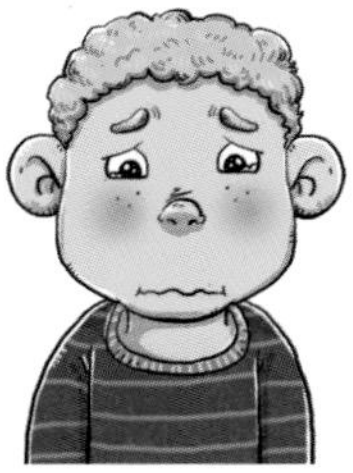

dad	sad
bag	tag
hat	cat
mat	bat

5.

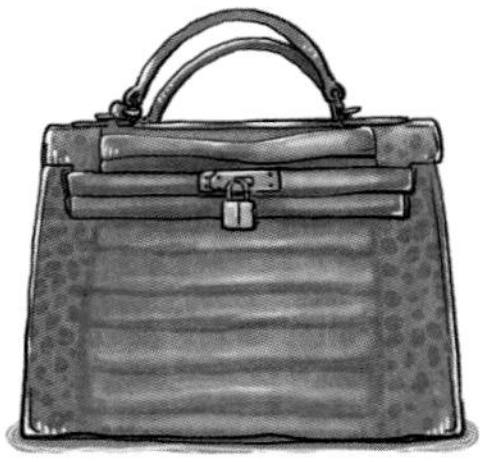

6.

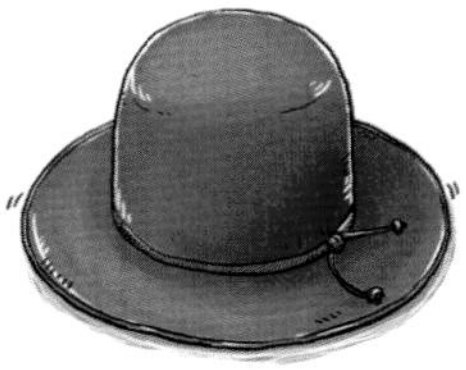

7.

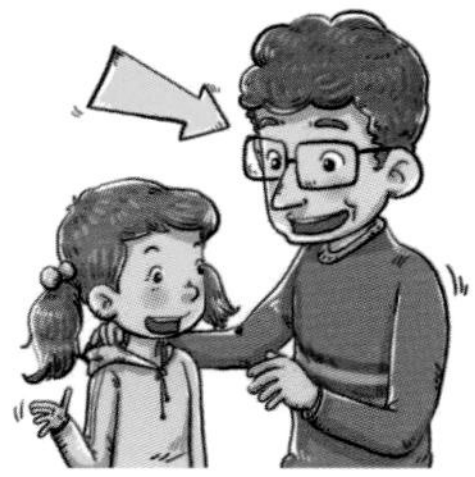

8.

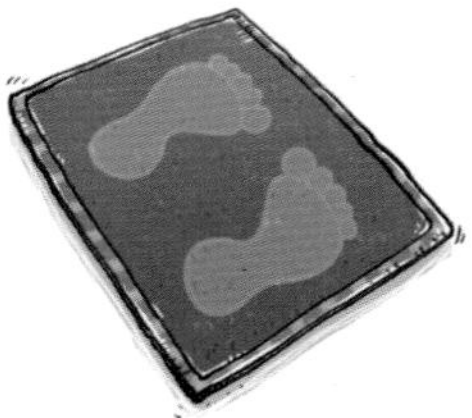

My dad  is on the mat .

He has a bag with a tag .

The cat is beside my dad .

She has a hat and a bat .

• Place the sticker on the shadow.

❃ Write the correct word.

| mat   sad   bat   tag   dad |

1

The cat is on the  _____ .

2

The cat has a  _____ .

3

The bag is beside my  _____ .

4

My dad is  _____ .

5

He has a hat with a _____ .

❀ Listen and repeat.

a n → an → c a n

-an

c a n → can

m a n → man

f a n → fan

p a n → pan

✿ Listen and repeat.

4001042

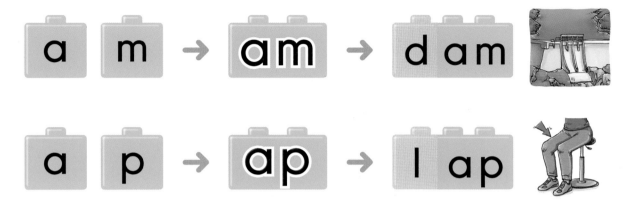

-am

d a m → dam   r a m → ram

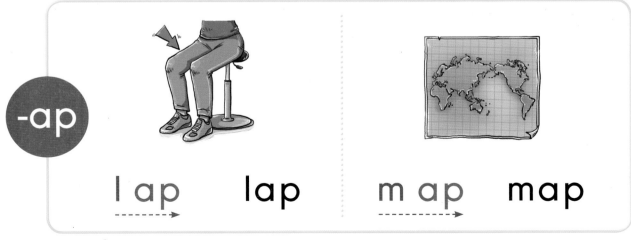

-ap

l a p → lap   m a p → map

Chant Along!

✿ Listen and circle the picture.

1.

fan   map

2.

ram   lap

3.

dam   can

4.

pan   man

5.

pan   map

6.

fan   can

❋ Listen and match.

1.

r

ap

am

2.

c

am

an

3.

m

ap

an

4.

f

an

ap

❋ Write the word using the rhyme.

-am   -an   -ap

1.

|

2.

f

3.

r

4.

m

✿ Listen and write -an, -am or -ap. Then match.

1.

   •

•

2.

   •

•

3.

   •

•

✿ Write the word that does not rhyme with the others.

1.

map
fan
can

2.

lap
map
ram

3.

ram
man
dam

Match the rhyme and the pictures. Then write.

-ap   -am   -an

m   r   f

l   d   m

A man 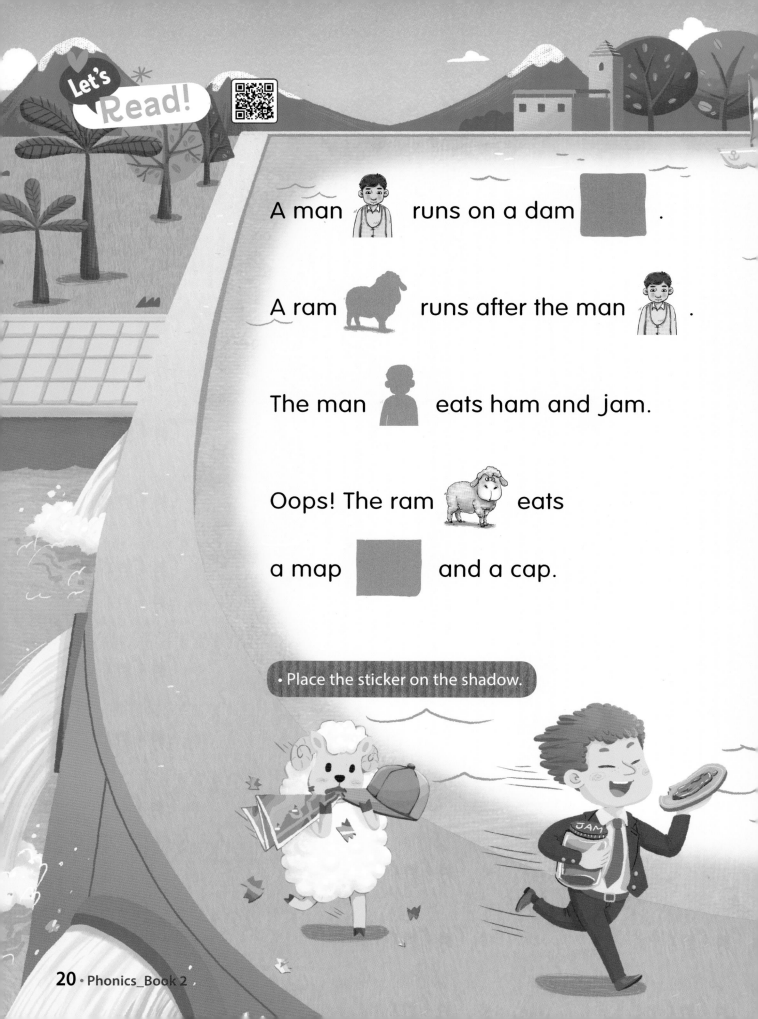 runs on a dam ▢ .

A ram runs after the man .

The man eats ham and jam.

Oops! The ram eats

a map ▢ and a cap.

• Place the sticker on the shadow.

✿ Write the correct word.

dam   man   ram   map   fan

1   The ram eats a _____.

2   A ram runs on a _____.

3   The man runs after the _____.

4   A _____ is on a map.

5   The _____ eats ham and jam.

✿ Listen and repeat.

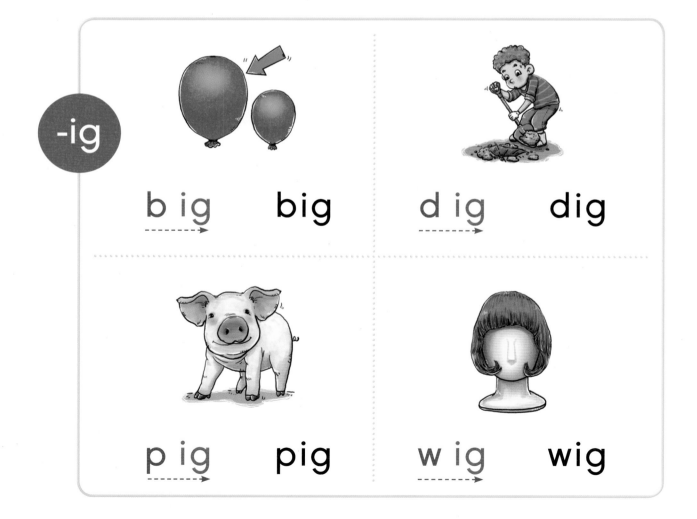

-ig

b ig   **big**

d ig   **dig**

p ig   **pig**

w ig   **wig**

✿ Listen and repeat.

i p → ip → l ip

-ip

l ip   lip

r ip   rip

d ip   dip

h ip   hip

Chant Along!

✿ Listen and circle the picture. Then match.

1.

hip   pig

2.

dig   lip

3.

rip   wig

4.

hip   dip

5.

dig   big

6.

dip   lip

✿ Listen and circle the rhyme.

1.

-ip   -ig

2.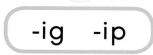

-ig   -ip

3.

-ip   -ig

4.

-ig   -ip

✿ Circle and write the word.

1.

w f a r i p l

_____

2.

c l w i g b n

_____

3.

t i m o b i g

_____

✿ Listen and circle the picture. Then write.

a r d i p g a w i g c o n r i p f z b i g m

1.

_____ _____ _____

2.

_____ _____ _____

3.

_____ _____ _____

4.

_____ _____ _____

✿ Match the rhyme and the pictures.

1. -ip ·

2.  -ig ·

✤ Write the word by using the letters.

Look at the pig  there.

He wears a big wig.

His lips are red.

His wig is yellow.

He digs a big hole.

• Place the sticker on the shadow.

✿ Circle and write the correct word.

1

The boy _____ S a hole.

dig   hip

2

The _____ wears a wig.

pig   dip

3

His _____ is big.

big   wig

4

His _____ wig is yellow.

dig   big

5

Her _____ S are red.

lip   rip

❋ Listen and repeat.

i n → in → b in

-in

b in → bin

p in → pin

ch in → chin

w in → win

✤ Listen and repeat.

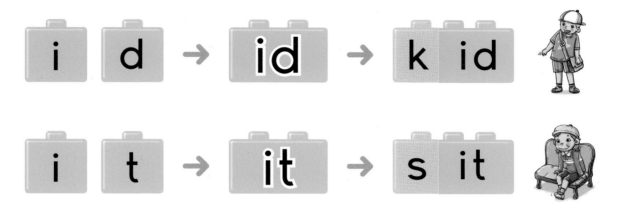

-id

k id → kid   l id → lid

-it

s it → sit   h it → hit

Chant Along!

✿ Listen and circle the picture. Then match.

1.

hit   sit

2.

pin   kid

3.

win   chin

4.

lid   hit

5.

bin   chin

6.

sit   pin

✿ Listen and circle the rhyme.

1.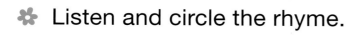

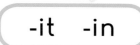

-it   -in

2.

-id   -it

3.

-it   -in

4.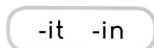

-id   -in

✿ Circle and write the word.

1.    k e m d w i n

---

2.    m u k i d l e

---

3.    i a z s i t p

---

✿ Listen and circle the picture. Then write.

f p c h i n w y s i t u n l k i d f w i n v

1.

___ ___ ___ ___

2.

___ ___ ___

3.

___ ___ ___

4.

___ ___ ___

✿ Match the rhyme and the pictures.

1. -in •　　••　　•

2. -id •　　••　　•

3. -it •　　••　　•

✿ Circle the six words in the puzzle. Then write each word under the picture.

1.

_____

- - - - - - - - - - - -

_____

2.

_____

- - - - - - - - - - - -

_____

3.

_____

- - - - - - - - - - - -

_____

4.

_____

- - - - - - - - - - - -

_____

5.

_____

- - - - - - - - - - - -

_____

6.

_____

- - - - - - - - - - - -

_____

a	c	q	d	s	i	t
l	i	d	u	g	a	e
p	t	k	i	d	h	f
i	l	u	v	j	i	g
n	k	w	i	n	t	h

Let's find Kevin.

Kevin sits on a bin.

Kevin has two pins on his hat.

Aha! That's Kevin,

the kid with a double chin.

• Place the sticker on the shadow.

✿ Circle and write the correct word.

1

Kevin sits on a _____.

| bin | lid |

2

That's Kevin, the _____ with a cap.

| win | kid |

3

The kid _____ S _____ on a bin.

| sit | hit |

4

He has a double _____.

| chin | pin |

5

He has a _____ on his hat.

| sit | pin |

✿ Match the rhyme and the pictures.

1. -ip

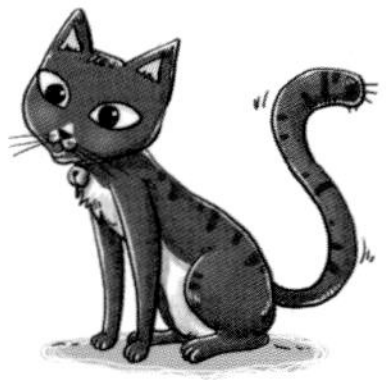
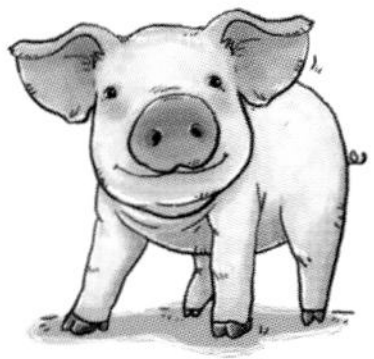

2. -at

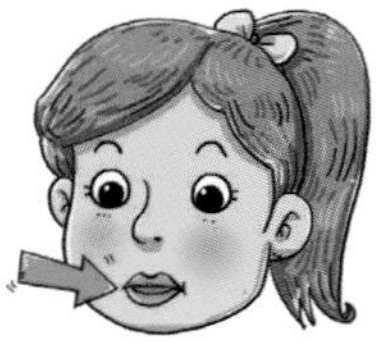
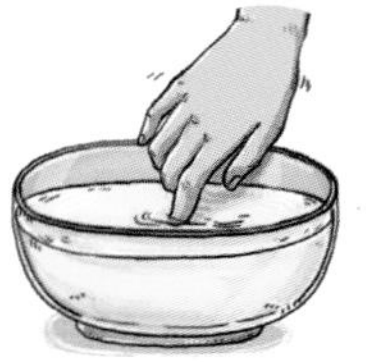

3. -ig

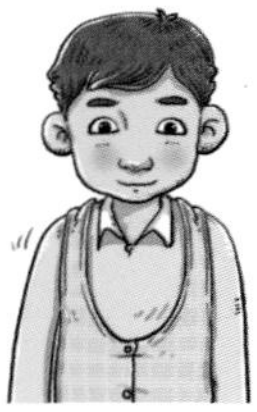
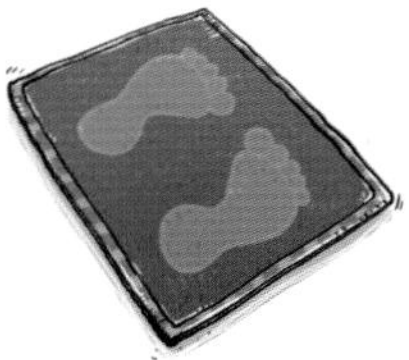

4. -an

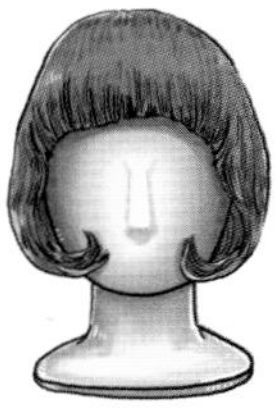
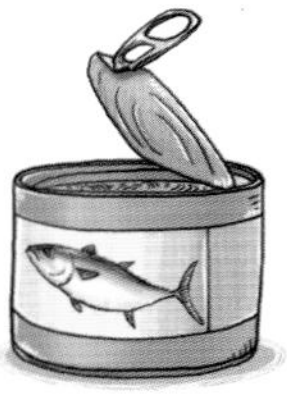

5. -ap

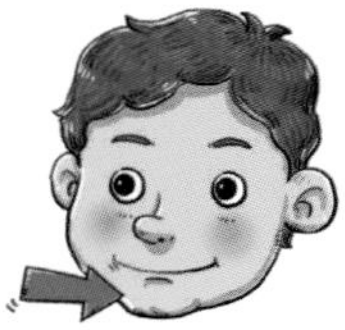
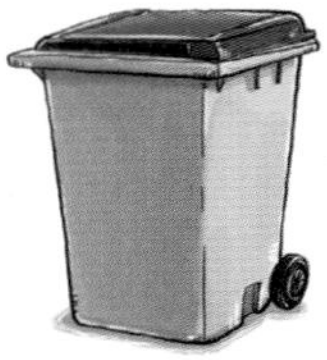

6. -in

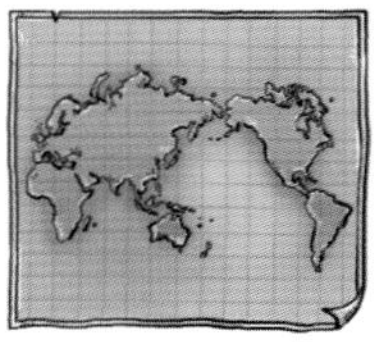
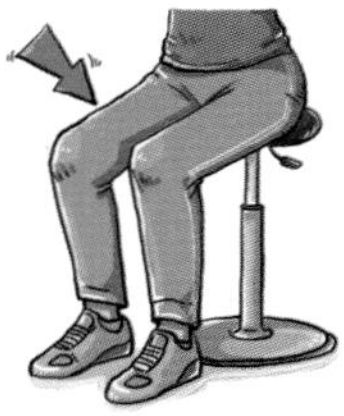

Listen and circle the word. Then match.

1. dad / sad

2. hit / sit

3. hip / rip

4. tag / bag

5. lid / kid

6. ram / dam

7. dig / wig

8. man / pan

✿ Listen and circle the picture. Then write.

1.

l

2.

h

3.

p

4.

b

5.

m

6.

d

Write the word in the puzzle.

1.

s
a
d

2.

3.

4.

5.

6.

7.

8.

9.

10.

11.

12.

✿ Listen and repeat.

-ug

b u g   **bug**   h u g   **hug**

m u g   **mug**   r u g   **rug**

✽ Listen and repeat.

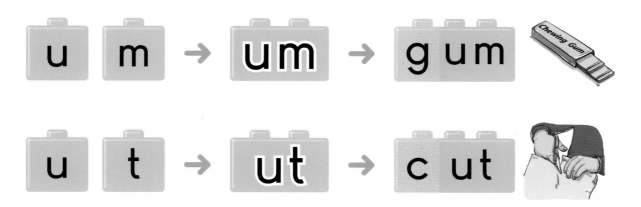

-um

g um → gum   dr um → drum

-ut

c ut → cut   h ut → hut

Chant Along!

✿ Listen and circle the picture.

1.

bug   gum

2.

cut   drum

3.

hug   rug

4.

gum   hut

5.

mug   drum

6.

hug   cut

✽ Listen and circle the rhyme.

1.
c	um
ug	ut

2.
g	ut
um	ug

3.
h	um
ut	ug

4.
r	um
ut	ug

5.
dr	ut
um	ug

6.
b	ug
ut	um

✽ Check the rhyme and write the word.

1.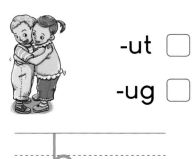

-ut ☐
-ug ☐

_____h_____

2.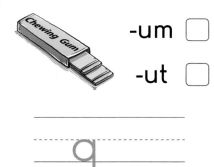

-um ☐
-ut ☐

_____g_____

3.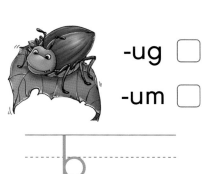

-ug ☐
-um ☐

_____b_____

4.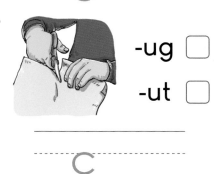

-ug ☐
-ut ☐

_____c_____

❀ Listen and write -ug, -um or -ut. Then match.

1.

g ___ ___ •

•

2.

m ___ ___ •

•

3.

h ___ ___ •

•

❀ Write the word that does not rhyme with the others.

1.

gum
cut
drum

2.

cut
hut
bug

3.

hug
drum
rug

✿ Write the word.

1.

_____
- - - - - - - - -
_____

2.

_____
- - - - - - - - -
_____

3.

_____
- - - - - - - - -
_____

4.

_____
- - - - - - - - -
_____

bug	hug
mug	rug
gum	drum
cut	hut

5.

_____
- - - - - - - - -
_____

6.

_____
- - - - - - - - -
_____

7.

_____
- - - - - - - - -
_____

8.

_____
- - - - - - - - -
_____

Many bugs have a party.

A bug plays the violin.

Another bug plays the drums.

Other bugs dance

on the rug .

One steps on the gum .

Oh, it can't move.

• Place the sticker on the shadow.

❋ Unscramble and write the word.

1
A [g b u] _____ plays the violin.

2
Kids [h g u] _____ each other.

3
Other bugs dance on the [u h t] _____.

4
A bug plays the [r m u d] _____.

5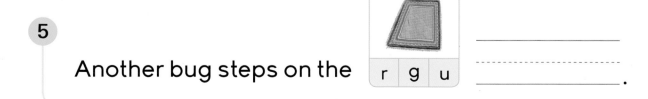
Another bug steps on the [r g u] _____.

❋ Listen and repeat.

u n → un → b un

-un

b un   bun

f un   fun

r un   run

s un   sun

✿ Listen and repeat.

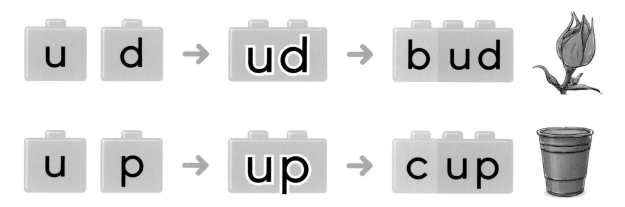

-ud

b ud   bud   m ud   mud

-up

c up   cup   p up   pup

Chant Along!

❀ Listen and circle the picture.

1. run   bud

2. bun   pup

3. cup   mud

4. sun   fun

5. run   pup

6. bud   sun

※ Listen and circle the rhyme.

1.
| s | ud |
| up | un |

2.
| p | up |
| un | ud |

3.
| r | un |
| up | ud |

4.
| c | un |
| ud | up |

5.
| b | ud |
| un | up |

6.
| m | un |
| up | ud |

※ Check the rhyme and write the word.

1.
-ud ☐
-up ☐

_____
c

2.
-un ☐
-ud ☐

_____
f

3.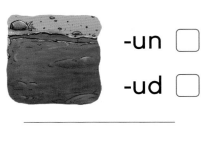
-un ☐
-ud ☐

_____
m

4.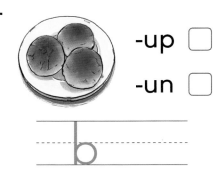
-up ☐
-un ☐

_____
b

❀ Listen and write -ud, -un or -up. Then match.

1.

p ___ ___   •   •

2.

b ___ ___   •   •

3.

f ___ ___   •   •

❀ Write the word that does not rhyme with the others.

1.

pup
run
cup

2.

mud

bun
sun
mud

3.

mud
cup
bud

✿ Match the rhyme and the pictures. Then write.

-ud

-un

-up

p
c

m
b

r
b

Two pups run and jump

in mud .

They smell rose buds .

They run home and

play in a tub.

They have buns and milk.

They have fun today.

• Place the sticker on the shadow.

✿ Unscramble and write the word.

1　Two pups play in ⬜ d m u ＿＿＿＿＿.

2　A pup has a ⬜ c p u ＿＿＿＿＿.

3　A pup smells a rose ⬜ u d b ＿＿＿＿＿.

4　The kid has ⬜ n u f ＿＿＿＿＿.

5　The kid ⬜ r n u ＿＿＿＿s home.

✿ Listen and repeat.

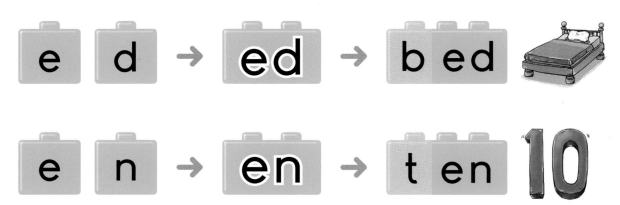

-ed

b ed   bed   r ed   red

-en

t en   ten   h en   hen

✿ Listen and repeat.

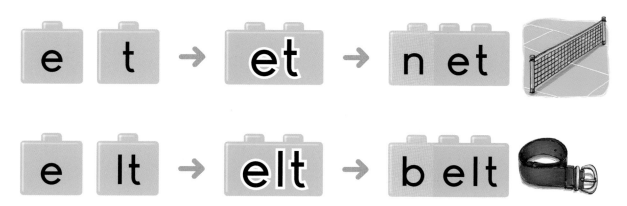

-et

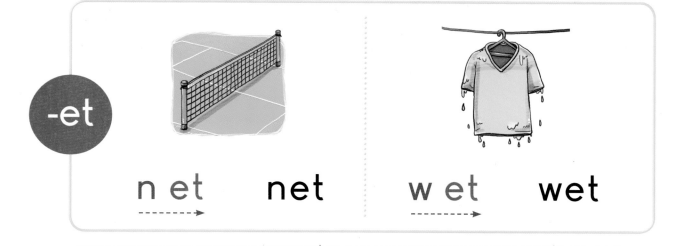

n et   net   w et   wet

-elt

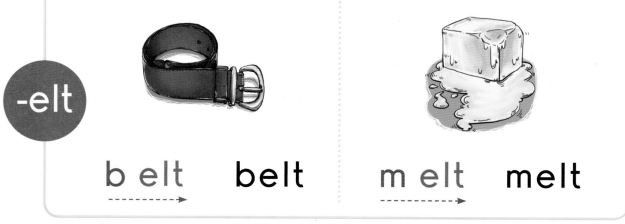

b elt   belt   m elt   melt

Chant Along!

✿ Listen and circle the picture. Then match.

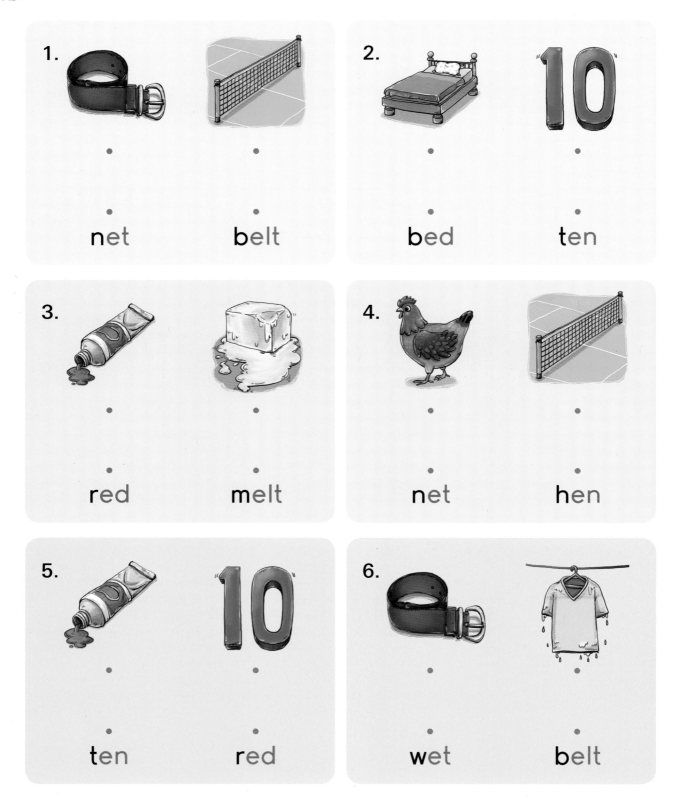

1.

net   belt

2.

bed   ten

3.

red   melt

4.

net   hen

5.

ten   red

6.

wet   belt

✽ Listen and circle the rhyme.

1.

-en   -elt

2.

-ed   -et

3.

-en   -ed

4.

-elt   -et

✽ Circle and write the word.

1.

f a d x b e d

_____

2.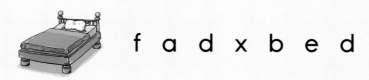

a m e l t r w

_____

3.

h e t e n k r

_____

✿ Listen and circle the picture. Then complete the word with -en, -ed, -et or -elt.

1.

b ___ ___

2.

t ___ ___

3.

n ___ ___

4.

m ___ ___ ___

✿ Match the rhyme and the picture.

1.
(**-en**)
•

2.
(**-ed**)
•

3.
(**-elt**)
•

4.
(**-et**)
•

•

•

•

•

✽ Write the word by using the letters.

-ed

_____
- - - - - -
_____

_____
- - - - - -
_____

-en

_____
- - - - - -
_____

_____
- - - - - -
_____

-et

_____
- - - - - -
_____

_____
- - - - - -
_____

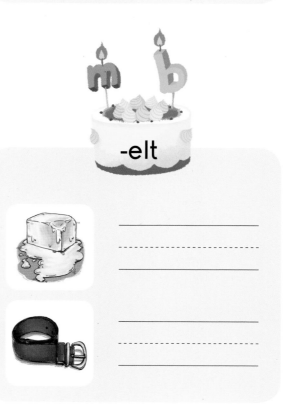

-elt

_____
- - - - - -
_____

_____
- - - - - -
_____

The snowman has a red  nose and

a red belt .

Ten **10** hens play around him.

Oh, it's raining.

The snowman is wet .

He melts .

• Place the sticker on the shadow.

✿ Write the correct word.

> melt   belt   net   red   hen

1 The snowman has a _____ hat.

2 The snowman has a _____ .

3 Ten hens play around the _____ .

4 A _____ is wet.

5 The snowman _____ s .

❁ Listen and repeat.

o p → op → h op

-op

h op   hop

c op   cop

m op   mop

t op   top

✿ Listen and repeat.

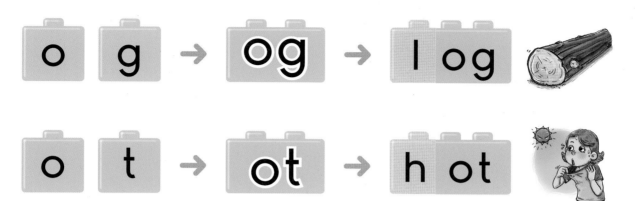

-og

l og   log   j og   jog

-ot

h ot   hot   p ot   pot

Chant Along!

✿ Listen and circle the picture. Then match.

1. hop top

2. jog cop

3. log pot

4. mop hot

5. top log

6. hot cop

✿ Listen and circle the rhyme.

1.

-op   -og

2.

-op   -ot

3.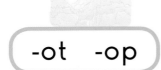

-ot   -op

4.

-og   -ot

✿ Circle and write the word.

1.    g c k p o t a   _____

2.    a l h o p n v   _____

3.    a b i u j o g   _____

✿ Listen and circle the picture. Then complete the word with -op, -og or -ot.

1.

m ___ ___

2.

p ___ ___

3.

j ___ ___

4.

h ___ ___

✿ Match the rhyme and the pictures.

1.  •   • •

2.  •   • •

3.   •   • •

✿ Circle the six words in the puzzle. Then write each word under the picture.

1.

_____

2.

_____

3.

_____

4.

_____

5.

_____

6.

_____

j	a	f	n	t	o	p
o	o	s	c	u	x	z	b
g	f	o	k	p	o	t
k	r	p	l	o	g	j
h	o	t	y	h	e	d

It's sunny and hot  .

A dog goes for a jog .

He jumps over the log .

Look! A cop follows.

Run! Run! Run away faster!

• Place the sticker on the shadow.

✿ Write the correct word.

> hot   cop   jog   hop   log

1 He jumps and  _____ _____ s .

2 A dog goes for a  _____ _____ .

3 It's _____ _____ .

4 A _____ _____ follows a dog.

5 A dog jumps over the  _____ _____ .

❋ Match the rhyme and the pictures.

1. -un ·   ·    ·   ·

2. -ug ·   ·    ·   ·

3. -ed ·   ·    ·   ·

4. -op ·   ·    ·   ·

5. -elt ·   ·    ·   ·

6. -ot ·   ·    ·   ·

✿ Listen and circle the picture.

1.

2.

3.

4.

5.

6.

✿ Listen and circle the word.

1. bud   hot   mud

2. red   wet   net

3. hug   jog   log

4. cut   mug   hut

5. top   pup   mop

6. bun   belt   rug

❀ Listen and write the word. Then match.

1. _____

   cop •

2. _____

   _r_ •

3. _____

   _h_ •

4. _____

   _w_ •

5. _____

   _b_ •

6. _____

   _s_ •

❀ Write the word in the puzzle.

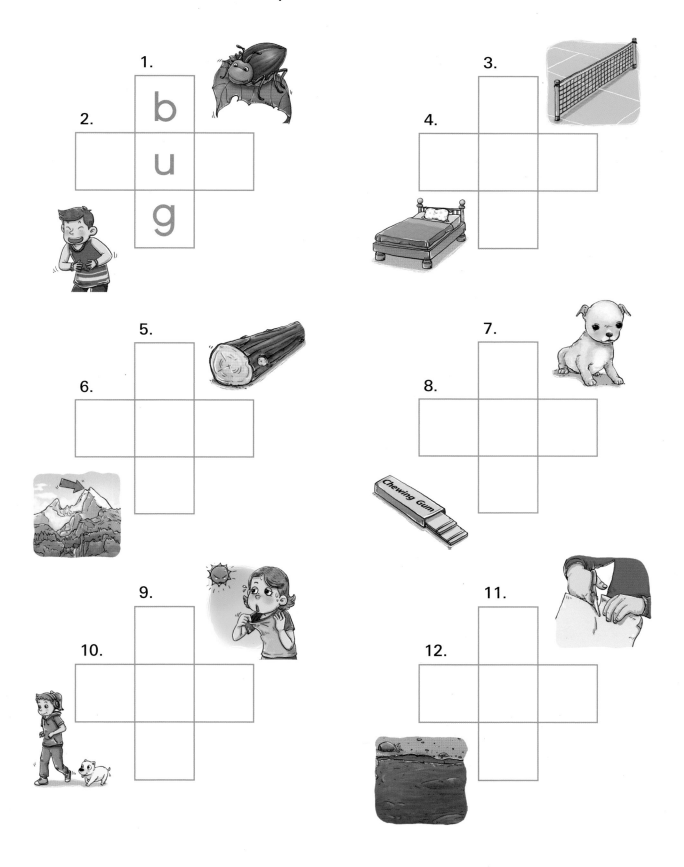

1.
2.

b
u
g

3.
4.

5.
6.

7.
8.

Chewing Gum

9.
10.

11.
12.

✿ Listen to the two words and circle the pictures.

1.

2.

3.

4.

✿ Listen and check the word.

1.
hug ☐
rug ☐

2.
top ☐
pot ☐

3.
bud ☐
man ☐

4.
lid ☐
lap ☐

5.
chin ☐
can ☐

6.
belt ☐
bag ☐

7.
pup ☐
hop ☐

8.
mat ☐
bug ☐

9.
ram ☐
lip ☐

10.
pig ☐
pan ☐

11.
lap ☐
dip ☐

12.
cut ☐
log ☐

✿ Circle and write the word.

f s w i n x r c b u d q l o g

1.

_____

- - - - - - - - - - - -

_____

2.

_____

- - - - - - - - - - - -

_____

3.

_____

- - - - - - - - - - - -

_____

m d r u m a b i g h c f a n p

4.

_____

- - - - - - - - - - - -

_____

5.

_____

- - - - - - - - - - - -

_____

6.

_____

- - - - - - - - - - - -

_____

s t e n k i s a d u j p i n o

7.

_____

- - - - - - - - - - - -

_____

8.

_____

- - - - - - - - - - - -

_____

9.

_____

- - - - - - - - - - - -

_____

❋ Match the picture and the sentence.

1.

A bug plays the drums.

2.

Two pups run and jump in mud.

3.

The cat has a hat and a bat.

4.

Kevin has two pins on his hat.

5.

The ram eats a map and a cap.

6.

The snowman has a red belt.

Roll a die and say a word with the ending sound.

Start

-at

-og

-un

-ip

-in

-an

-up

-ad

Wait one turn.

Go ahead 3 spaces.

-id

-ut

-it

-op

-en

-elt

Go back to "Start."

✿ Listen and check the correct number for the picture.

1.

2.

3.

4.

5.

6.

7.

8.

9.

10.

❋ Write the correct word for the picture.

11.

r _____

12.

c _____

13.

b _____

14.

h _____

15.

m _____

16.

c _____

17.

h _____

18.

s _____

19.

b _____

20.

d _____

Syllabus   Short Vowels

Period	Unit	Target Sounds	Target Words
1	**Unit 1**	at, ad, ag	hat, cat, mat, bat, dad, sad, bag, tag
2			
3	**Unit 2**	an, am, ap	can, man, fan, pan, dam, ram, lap, map
4			
5	**Unit 3**	ig, ip	big, dig, pig, wig, lip, rip, dip, hip
6			
7	**Unit 4**	in, id, it	bin, pin, chin, win, kid, lid, sit, hit
8			
9	**Review 1**	Short vowel a, i	
10	**Unit 5**	ug, um, ut	bug, hug, mug, rug, gum, drum, cut, hut
11			
12	**Unit 6**	un, ud, up	bun, fun, run, sun, bud, mud, cup, pup
13			
14	**Unit 7**	ed, en, et, elt	bed, red, ten, hen, net, wet, belt, melt
15			
16	**Unit 8**	op, og, ot	hop, cop, mop, top, log, jog, hot, pot
17			
18	**Review 2**	Short vowel u, e, o	
19	**Challenge**	Short vowel a, i, u, e, o	
20			

Answers

Student Book **Answers**

• Unit 1

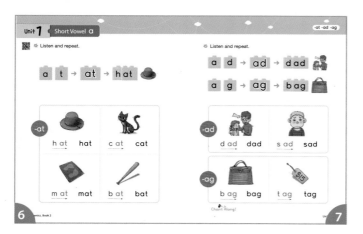

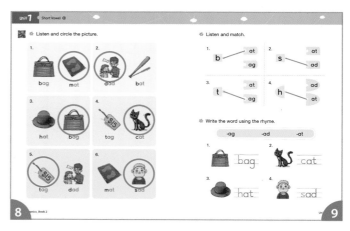

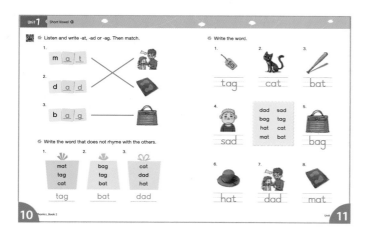

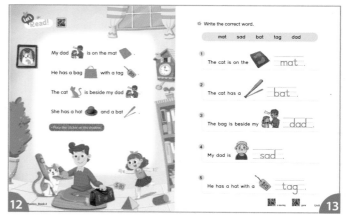

• Unit 2

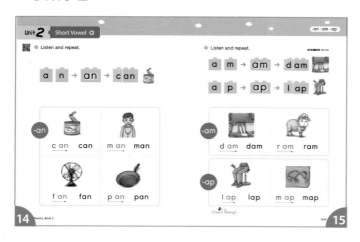

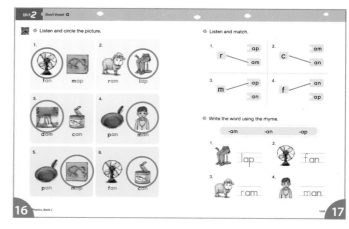

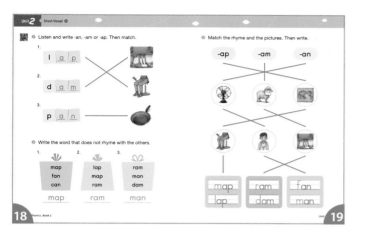

Unit 3

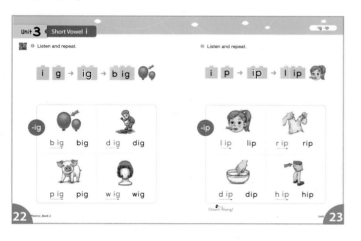

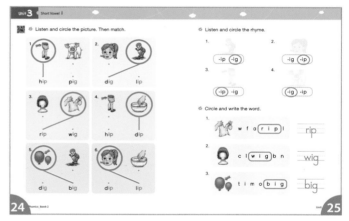

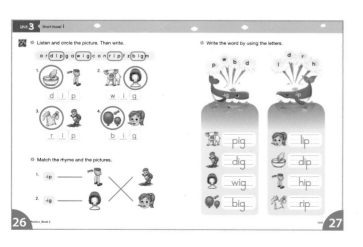

Student Book **Answers**

• Unit 4

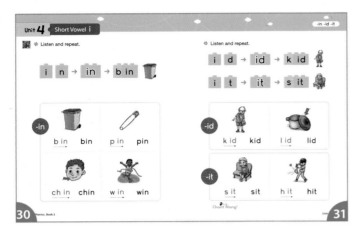

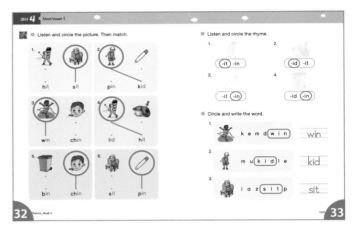

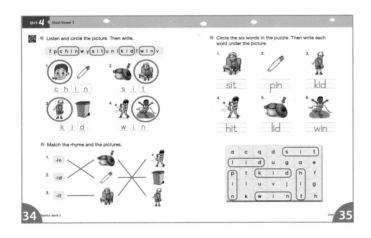

• Review 1

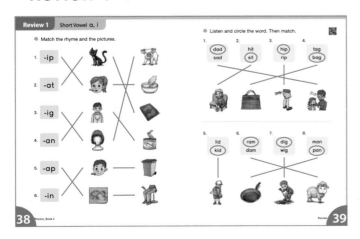

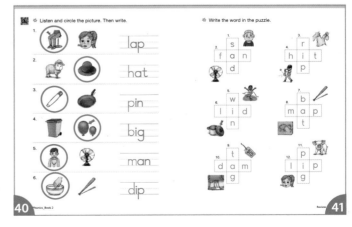

90 • Phonics_Book 2

• Unit 5

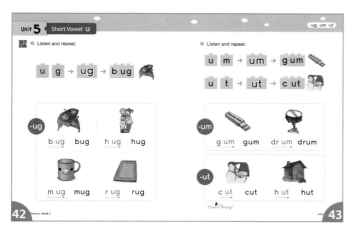

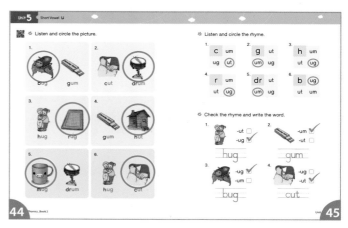

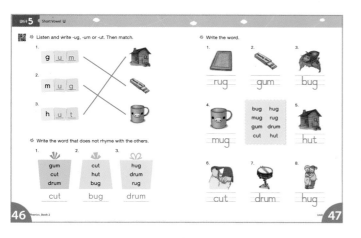

• Unit 6

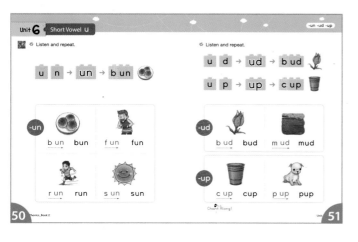

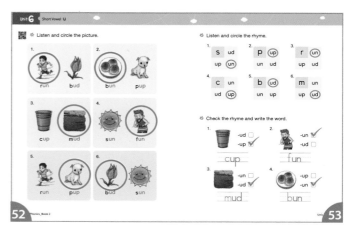

Student Book **Answers**

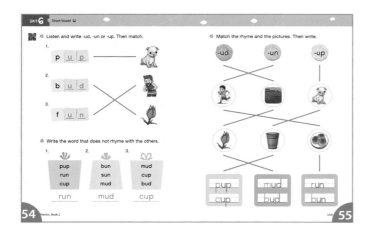

• Unit 7

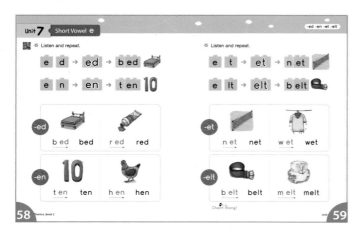

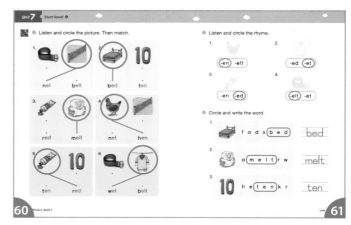

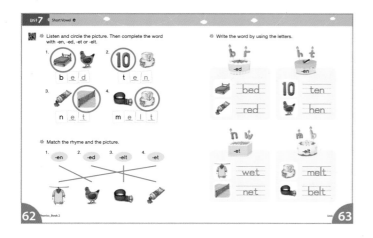

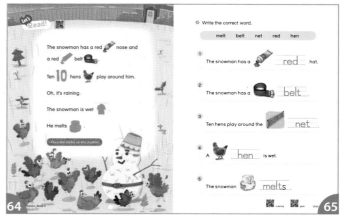

Unit 8

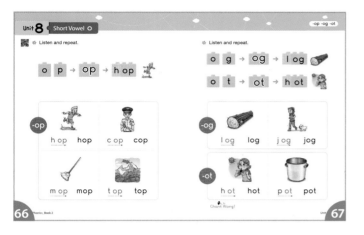

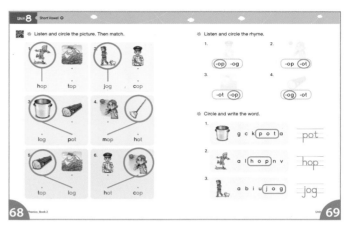

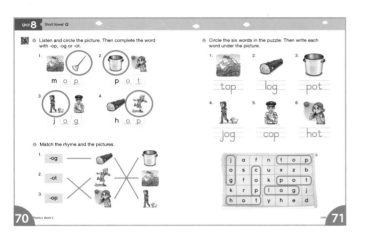

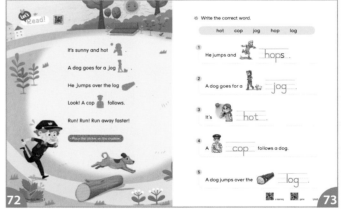

Review 2

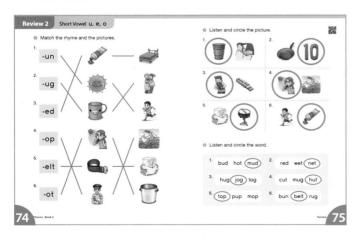

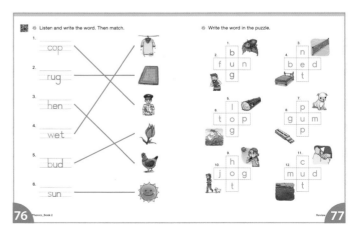

Student Book **Answers**

• Challenge

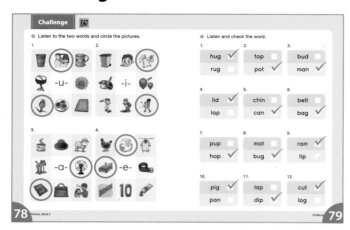

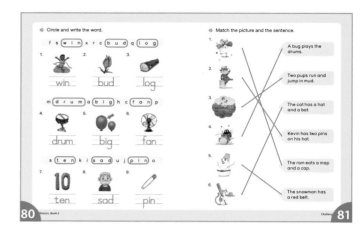

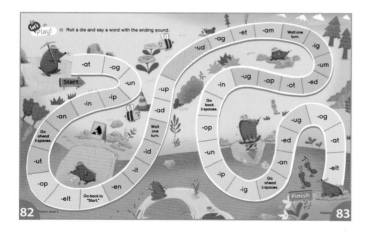

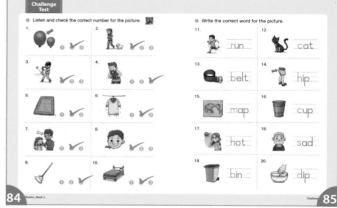

Workbook **Answers**

• Unit 1

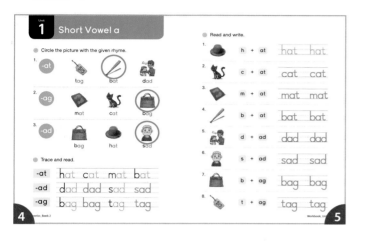

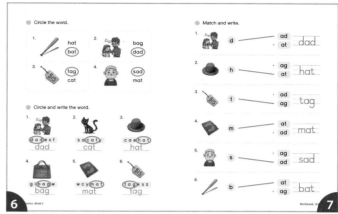

• Unit 2

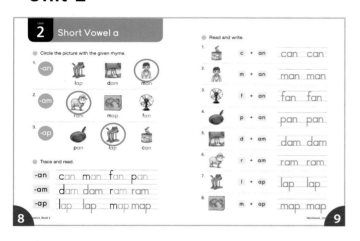

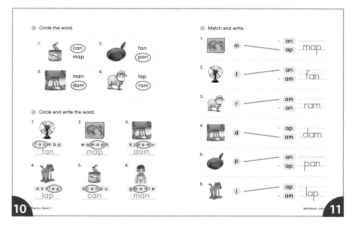

• Unit 3

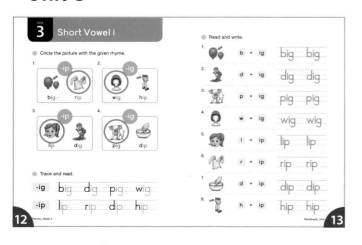

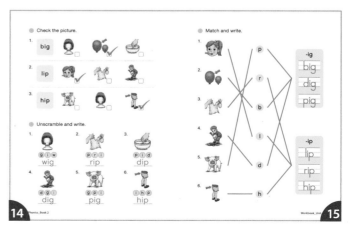

Workbook **Answers**

• Unit 4

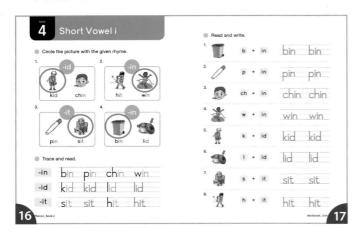

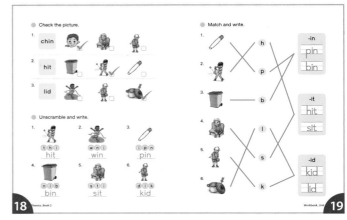

• Review 1

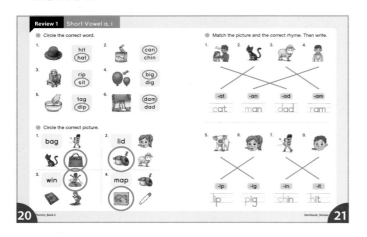

• Unit 5

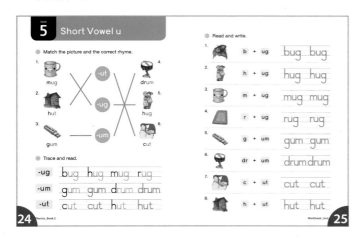

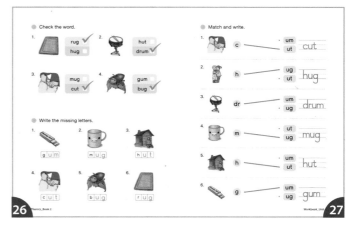

• Unit 6

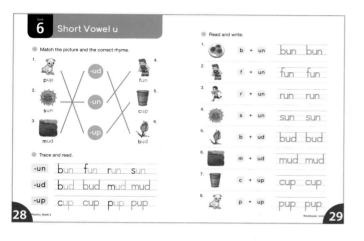

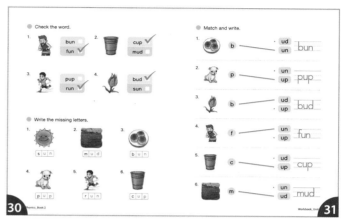

• Unit 7

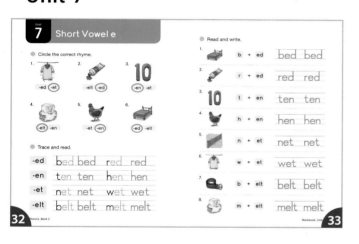

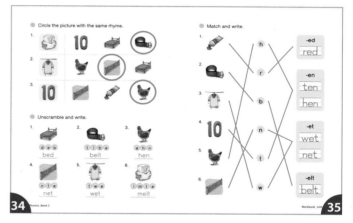

• Unit 8

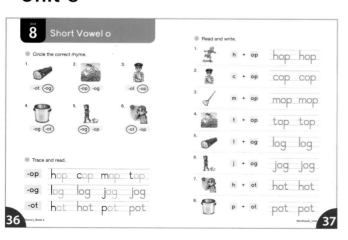

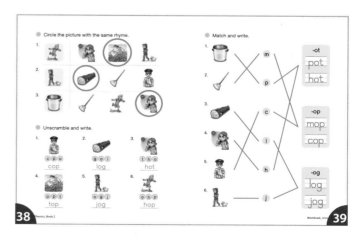

Workbook **Answers**

• Review 2

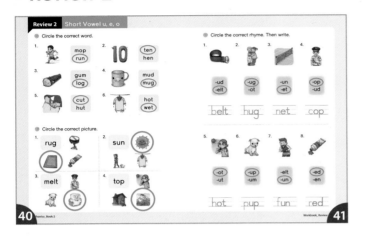

Final Test **Answers**

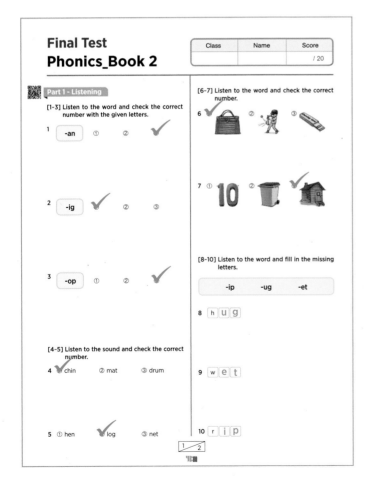

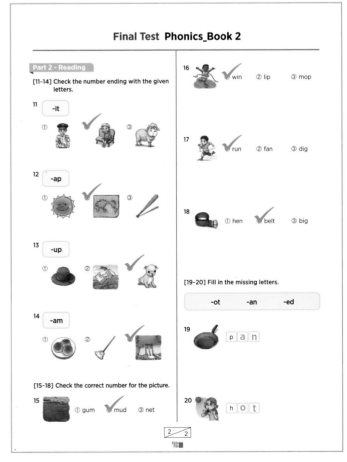

-at

-at

-at

-at

-ad

-ad

-ag

-ag

cat	hat
bat	mat
sad	dad
tag	bag

WORD CARDS

-an

-an

-an

-an

-am

-am

-ap

-ap

man	can
pan	fan
ram	dam
map	lap

-ig

-ig

-ig

-ig

-ip

-ip

-ip

-ip

dig	big
wig	pig
rip	lip
hip	dip

WORD CARDS

-in

-in

-in

-in

-id

-id

-it

-it

pin	bin
win	chin
lid	kid
hit	sit

-ug

-ug

-ug

-ug

-um

-um

-ut

-ut

hug	bug
rug	mug
drum	gum
hut	cut

WORD CARDS

-un

-un

-un

-un

-ud

-ud

-up

-up

fun	bun
sun	run
mud	bud
pup	cup

-ed

-ed

-en

-en

-et

-et

-elt

-elt

red	bed
hen	ten
wet	net
melt	belt

-op

-op

-op

-op

-og

-og

-ot

-ot

cop	hop
top	mop
jog	log
pot	hot

Unit 1
p.12

Unit 2
p.20

Unit 3
p.28

Unit 4
p.36

Unit 5
p.48

Unit 6
p.56

Unit 7
p.64

Unit 8
p.72

PHONICS LAND

Short Vowels

WORKBOOK

BOOK **2**

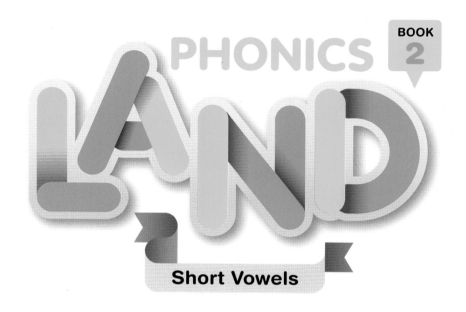

PHONICS
BOOK
2
LAND
Short Vowels

WORKBOOK

Contents

Short Vowel a

◎ Circle the picture with the given rhyme.

1. **-at**

 tag   bat   dad

2. **-ag**

 mat   cat   bag

3. **-ad**

bag   hat   sad

◎ Trace and read.

-at	hat cat mat bat
-ad	dad sad
-ag	bag tag

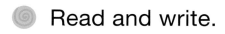 **Read and write.**

1.   h + at   hat   hat

2.   c + at

3.   m + at

4.   b + at

5.   d + ad

6.   s + ad

7.   b + ag

8.   t + ag

◎ Circle the word.

1. hat
   bat

2. bag
   dad

3. tag
   cat

4. sad
   mat

◎ Circle and write the word.

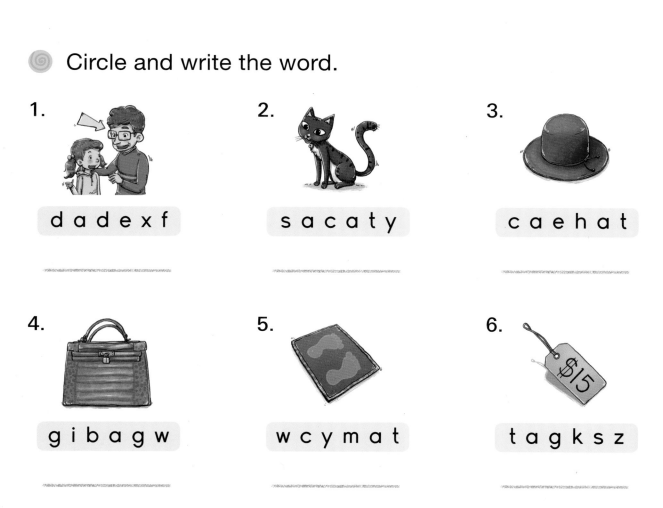

1. d a d e x f
   _____

2. s a c a t y
   _____

3. c a e h a t
   _____

4. g i b a g w
   _____

5. w c y m a t
   _____

6. t a g k s z
   _____

Match and write.

1. d •
   • ad _____
   • at - - - - - - -

2. h •
   • ag _____
   • at - - - - - - -

3. t •
   • ad _____
   • ag - - - - - - -

4. m •
   • at _____
   • ad - - - - - - -

5. s •
   • ag _____
   • ad - - - - - - -

6. b •
   • at _____
   • ag - - - - - - -

◎ Circle the picture with the given rhyme.

1. **-an**

lap

dam

man

2. **-am**

ram

map

fan

3. **-ap**

pan

lap

can

◎ Trace and read.

-an	can man fan pan
-am	dam ram
-ap	lap map

🌀 Read and write.

1. c + an _____

2. m + an _____

3. f + an _____

4. p + an _____

5. d + am _____

6. r + am _____

7. l + ap _____

8. m + ap _____

Circle the word.

1.   can
     map

2.   fan
     pan

3.   man
     dam

4.   lap
     ram

Circle and write the word.

1.   f a n m b p

2.   w q m a p h

3.   k j d a m v

4.   a s r l a p

5.   z c a n p u

6.   g m a n l e

Match and write.

1. m •
     • an _____
     • ap _____

2. f •
     • an _____
     • am _____

3. r •
     • am _____
     • an _____

4. d •
     • ap _____
     • am _____

5. p •
     • an _____
     • ap _____

6. l •
     • ap _____
     • am _____

Short Vowel i

 Circle the picture with the given rhyme.

1.

-ip

big   rip

2.

-ig

wig   hip

3.

-ip

lip   dig

4.

-ig

pig   dip

 Trace and read.

-ig   big dig pig wig

-ip   lip rip dip hip

Read and write.

1. 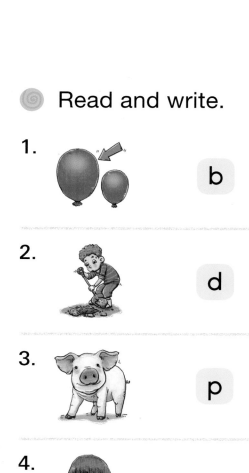 **b** + **ig** _____

2. **d** + **ig** _____

3. **p** + **ig** _____

4. **w** + **ig** _____

5. **l** + **ip** _____

6. **r** + **ip** _____

7. **d** + **ip** _____

8. **h** + **ip** _____

@ Check the picture.

1. | big | | □ | | □ | | □ |

2. | lip | | □ | | □ | | □ |

3. | hip | | □ | | □ | | □ |

@ Unscramble and write.

1.

(g)(i)(w)

_____

2.

(p)(r)(i)

_____

3.

(p)(i)(d)

_____

4.

(d)(g)(i)

_____

5.

(g)(p)(i)

_____

6.

(i)(h)(p)

_____

Match and write.

1.

2.

3.

4.

5.

6.

p

r

b

l

d

h

-ig

-ip

Short Vowel i

🌀 Circle the picture with the given rhyme.

1.
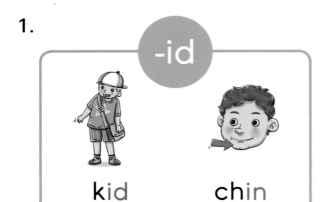

-id

kid   chin

2.

-in

hit   win

3.

-it

pin   sit

4.

-in

bin   lid

🌀 Trace and read.

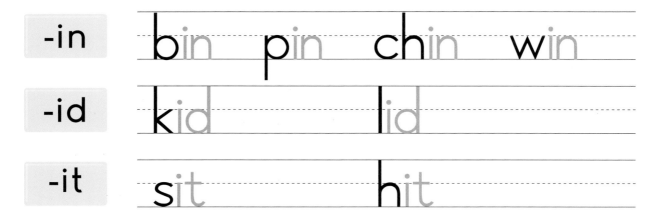

-in	bin pin chin win
-id	kid lid
-it	sit hit

Read and write.

1. b + in _____

2. p + in _____

3. ch + in _____

4. w + in _____

5. k + id _____

6. l + id _____

7. s + it _____

8. h + it _____

Check the picture.

1. chin □  □  □

2. hit □  □  □

3. lid □  □  □

Unscramble and write.

1.

   t h i

2.

   w n i

3.

   i p n

4.

   n i b

5.

   s t i

6.

   d i k

Match and write.

1.

h

-in

_____
- - - - - - - -
_____
- - - - - - - -

2.

p

3.

b

-it

_____
- - - - - - - -
_____
- - - - - - - -

4.

l

5.

s

-id

_____
- - - - - - - -
_____
- - - - - - - -

6.

k

◎ Circle the correct word.

1.

   hit
   hat

2.

   can
   chin

3.

   rip
   sit

4.

   big
   dig

5.

   tag
   dip

6.

   dam
   dad

◎ Circle the correct picture.

1. bag

2. lid

3. win

4. map

Match the picture and the correct rhyme. Then write.

1.

2.

3.

4.

-at

-an

-ad

-am

c

m

d

r

5.

6.

7.

8.

-ip

-ig

-in

-it

l

p

ch

h

◉ Circle the picture with the same rhyme.

1.

2.

3.

4.

◉ Write the missing letters.

1.

m ☐ ☐

2.

l ☐ ☐

3.

s ☐ ☐

4.

p ☐ ☐

5.

l ☐ ☐

6.

d ☐ ☐

7.

m ☐ ☐

8.

w ☐ ☐

◎ Write the word.

1.

_____
- - - - - - - - - - - - -
_____

2.

_____
- - - - - - - - - - - - -
_____

3.

_____
- - - - - - - - - - - - -
_____

4.

_____
- - - - - - - - - - - - -
_____

5.

_____
- - - - - - - - - - - - -
_____

6.

_____
- - - - - - - - - - - - -
_____

7.

_____
- - - - - - - - - - - - -
_____

8.

_____
- - - - - - - - - - - - -
_____

9.

_____
- - - - - - - - - - - - -
_____

10.

_____
- - - - - - - - - - - - -
_____

11.

_____
- - - - - - - - - - - - -
_____

12.

_____
- - - - - - - - - - - - -
_____

🌀 Match the picture and the correct rhyme.

1.

mug

• • -ut •

• 4.
drum

2.

hut

• • -ug •

• 5.
hug

3.

gum

• • -um •

• 6.
cut

🌀 Trace and read.

-ug	bug hug mug rug
-um	gum drum
-ut	cut hut

🌀 **Read and write.**

1. b + ug _____

2. h + ug _____

3. m + ug _____

4. r + ug _____

5. g + um _____

6. dr + um _____

7. c + ut _____

8. h + ut _____

Check the word.

1.  rug ☐
   hug ☐

2.  hut ☐
   drum ☐

3.  mug ☐
   cut ☐

4.  gum ☐
   bug ☐

Write the missing letters.

1.  g | |

2.  m | |

3.  h | |

4.  c | |

5.  b | |

6.  r | |

Match and write.

1. c •
   • um _____
   • ut _____

2. h •
   • ug _____
   • ut _____

3. dr •
   • um _____
   • ug _____

4. m •
   • ut _____
   • ug _____

5. h •
   • um _____
   • ut _____

6. g •
   • um _____
   • ug _____

Match the picture and the correct rhyme.

1.

pup

· ·  ·

-ud

·

fun

4.

2.

sun

· ·  ·

-un

·

cup

5.

3.

mud

· ·  ·

-up

·

bud

6.

Trace and read.

-un	bun fun run sun
-ud	bud mud
-up	cup pup

Read and write.

1. b + un _____

2. f + un _____

3. r + un _____

4. s + un _____

5. b + ud _____

6. m + ud _____

7. c + up _____

8. p + up _____

Check the word.

1.

| bun | ☐ |
| fun | ☐ |

2.

| cup | ☐ |
| mud | ☐ |

3.

| pup | ☐ |
| run | ☐ |

4.

| bud | ☐ |
| sun | ☐ |

Write the missing letters.

1.

s ☐ ☐

2.

m ☐ ☐

3.

b ☐ ☐

4.

p ☐ ☐

5.

r ☐ ☐

6.

c ☐ ☐

Match and write.

1.
b •
  • ud _____
  • un _____

2.
p •
  • un _____
  • up _____

3.
b •
  • ud _____
  • up _____

4.
f •
  • un _____
  • up _____

5.
c •
  • ud _____
  • up _____

6.
m •
  • un _____
  • ud _____

Short Vowel e

🌀 Circle the correct rhyme.

1.

   -ed   -et

2.

   -elt   -ed

3.

   -en   -et

4.

   -elt   -en

5.

   -et   -en

6.

   -ed   -elt

🌀 Trace and read.

-ed	bed	red
-en	ten	hen
-et	net	wet
-elt	belt	melt

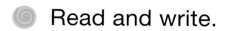 **Read and write.**

1.   b + ed

2.   r + ed

3.   t + en

4.   h + en

5.   n + et

6.   w + et

7.   b + elt

8.   m + elt

Circle the picture with the same rhyme.

1.

2.

3.

Unscramble and write.

1. d e b

2. t l b e

3. e h n

4. n t e

5. t w e

6. l m t e

◎ Match and write.

1.

• h •

-ed
_____
- - - - - - - - - -
_____

2.

• r •

-en
_____
- - - - - - - - - -
_____

_____
- - - - - - - - - -
_____

3.

• b •

4.

• n •

-et
_____
- - - - - - - - - -
_____

_____
- - - - - - - - - -
_____

5.

• t •

6.

• w •

-elt
_____
- - - - - - - - - -
_____

◎ Circle the correct rhyme.

1.

-ot   -og

2.

-op   -og

3.

-ot   -op

4.

-og   -ot

5.

-og   -op

6.

-ot   -op

◎ Trace and read.

-op	hop cop mop top
-og	log jog
-ot	hot pot

Read and write.

1.  h + op _____

2. c + op _____

3.  m + op _____

4. t + op _____

5. l + og _____

6. j + og _____

7. h + ot _____

8. p + ot _____

Circle the picture with the same rhyme.

1.

2.

3.

Unscramble and write.

1.

c p o

_____

2.

g o l

_____

3.

t h o

_____

4.

o p t

_____

5.

o g j

_____

6.

o h p

_____

Match and write.

1.

2.

3.

4.

5.

6.

m

p

c

l

h

j

-ot

-op

-og

◎ Circle the correct word.

1.

mop
run

2.

ten
hen

3.

gum
log

4.

mud
mug

5.

cut
hut

6.

hot
wet

◎ Circle the correct picture.

1. rug

2. sun

3. melt

4. top

Circle the correct rhyme. Then write.

1.

-ud
-elt

b____

2.

-ug
-ot

h____

3.

-un
-et

n____

4.

-op
-ud

c____

5.

-ot
-ut

h____

6.

-up
-um

p____

7.

-elt
-un

f____

8.

-ed
-en

r____

Circle the picture with the same rhyme.

1.

2.

3.
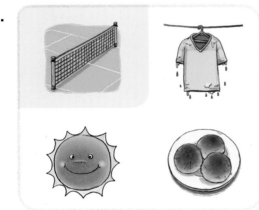

4.

Write the missing letters.

1.

| j | | |

2.

| h | | |

3.

| b | | |

4.

| t | | |

5.

| c | | |

6.

| h | | |

7.

| p | | |

8.

| b | | |

Write the word.

1.

2.

3.

4.

5.

6.

7.

8.

9.

10.

11.

12.

Memo